Piano Exam Pieces

ABRSM Grade 2

Selected from the 2017 & 2018 syllabus

Name

Date of exam

C000126890

Contents

Editor for ABRSM: Richard Jones

First published in 2016 by ABRSM (Publishing) Ltd, a wholly owned subsidiary of ABRSM, 24 Portland Place, London W1B 1LU, United Kingdom
© 2016 by The Associated Board of the Royal Schools of Music
Distributed worldwide by Oxford University Press

Music origination by Julia Bovee
Cover by Kate Benjamin & Andy Potts
Printed in England by Halstan & Co. Ltd, Amersham, Bucks., on materials from sustainable sources.

A:1

Allegretto

First movement from Sonatina No. 3 in F

Thomas Attwood
(1765–1838)

The English composer and organist Thomas Attwood sang in the choir of the Chapel Royal from the age of nine. He studied in Naples and then with Mozart in Vienna (1785–7). After his return to England he became music tutor to the royal family and later organist of St Paul's Cathedral and composer to the Chapel Royal.

  This piece illustrates his graceful, elegant style that often seems to owe much to Mozart. When he was studying in Vienna, Mozart said of him: 'He partakes more of my style than any scholar I ever had; and I predict that he will prove a sound musician.' All dynamics and slurs are editorial suggestions only.

Source: *Easy Progressive Lessons Fingered for Young Beginners on the Piano Forte or Harpsichord* (London, *c*.1795)

© 1983 by The Associated Board of the Royal Schools of Music
Adapted from Attwood: *Easy Progressive Lessons*, edited by Richard Jones (ABRSM)

For a Girl or a Woman

Ein Mädchen oder Weibchen

from *Die Zauberflöte*, K. 620

A:2

Arranged by Christopher Norton

W. A. Mozart
(1756–91)

In Mozart's 1791 opera *Die Zauberflöte* (The Magic Flute), this tune is sung by a comic character called Papageno, the queen's bird-catcher. He accompanies the hero Tamino in his quest to rescue the queen's daughter Pamina, who has been abducted. To protect them, Tamino is given a magic flute, and Papageno magic bells. In the aria arranged here for piano, Papageno longs to meet the girl of his dreams, who later turns out to be Papagena. He accompanies the song on his magic bells, which in the opera are played on the glockenspiel.

La Mourisque

Arranged by Martin White

Tylman Susato
(*c.*1510/15–*c.*1570)

Tylman Susato was a town musician in Antwerp, where he ran a flourishing music publishing business. His attractive instrumental dances, published in 1551, are simple arrangements of well-known chansons (French songs for several voices in parts). In this dance, the upper left-hand C in bb. 17, 21 and 25 may be omitted.

© 2015 by The Associated Board of the Royal Schools of Music
Reproduced from *Piano Mix 2*, compiled and edited by David Blackwell (ABRSM)

Song

Second movement from Serenade, Op. 183 No. 1

Carl Reinecke
(1824–1910)

The German composer Carl Reinecke built up a fine reputation as a pianist in Germany and Scandinavia during the 1840s and 1850s. In the late 19th century he settled in Leipzig as professor (later director) of the conservatory and conductor of the Gewandhaus Orchestra.

Reinecke's piano music includes many pieces for children, such as *Fünf Serenaden für die Jugend* (Five Serenades for the Young), Op. 183, from which this movement is selected. As the title suggests, this is a song-like piece in style and texture. Being written for the piano only, it belongs to the tradition of Mendelssohn's *Lieder ohne Worte* (songs without words).

Source: *Fünf Clavier-Serenaden für die Jugend*, Op. 183 (Leipzig, 1885)

B:2

Waltz in G

No. 2 from *Poklad melodií*, Vol. 2

Bedřich Smetana
(1824–84)

Bedřich Smetana settled in Prague in 1843, where he taught the piano and studied theory and composition. After the premiere in 1866 of his most famous work, the opera *Prodaná nevěsta* (The Bartered Bride), he was appointed chief conductor of the Provisional Theatre, a post he retained until 1874, when he became deaf. Despite this disability, over the next five years he composed his famous cycle of six symphonic poems *Má vlast* (My Fatherland) and his most important chamber work, the string quartet *Z mého života* (From My Life).

Smetana also composed a significant amount of piano music, including the two volumes of *Poklad melodií* (Treasure of Melodies), which date from 1849–50. The second piece from Vol. 2, selected here, is unnamed in the source. Here it is given an editorial title that reflects its dance style. The dynamics in bb. 1–21 are editorial suggestions only.

Source: autograph MS, National Museum of Prague, Czech Museum of Music, Bedřich Smetana Museum, S 217/1357

The Stowaway

No. 7 from *Ship Ahoy!*

B:3

Stanley Wilson
(1899–1953)

Ship Ahoy! is made up of twelve nautical scenes for the piano. 'The Stowaway', selected here, is a play on 'Down among the dead men', an English traditional song attributed to John Dyer (1700–58). The piece is to be played *pianissimo* throughout, and one can imagine the stowaway hiding deep down in the hold of the ship, perhaps aware of the sailors asleep in their berths. The tomb-like atmosphere might explain the reference to the 'dead men'. Although the published metronome mark is ♩ = 132, candidates may prefer a more relaxed tempo, such as ♩ = c.108.

Stanley Wilson was a student at London's Royal College of Music (1915–21, with an interruption for war service), studying composition with Stanford and conducting with Boult. In later years, he taught at Ipswich Grammar School and Dulwich College.
Source: *Ship Ahoy!* (Manchester: Forsyth, 1932)

The Piper o' Dundee

Arranged by Richard Michael

Trad. Scottish

The arranger, Richard Michael, tells us that 'This traditional Scottish folk song should be played as if marching to the bagpipes.' The Piper of Dundee was a prominent Jacobite – in other words, he followed the exiled King James VII of Scotland (who was also King James II of England and father of the 'Old Pretender'). He is said to have attracted many followers to the Jacobite cause, which was led by his master Viscount Dundee (John Graham of Claverhouse). As a result, Dundee managed to raise a Jacobite army large enough to defeat the English government forces at the Battle of Killiecrankie in 1689.

The Cat

from *Peter and the Wolf*, Op. 67

C:2

Arranged by David Blackwell

Sergey Prokofiev
(1891–1953)

Moderato ♩ = *c*.88
Suddenly, something caught Peter's eye.
He saw a cat crawling through the long grass.

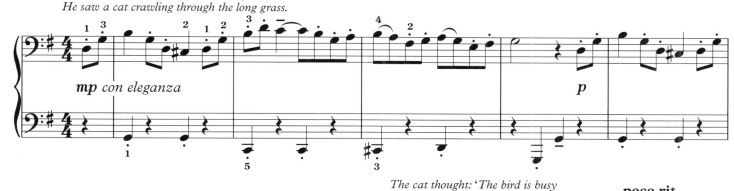

The cat thought: 'The bird is busy arguing. I'll just grab him.'

poco rit.

Stealthily…

a tempo
…she crept towards him on her velvet paws.

rall.

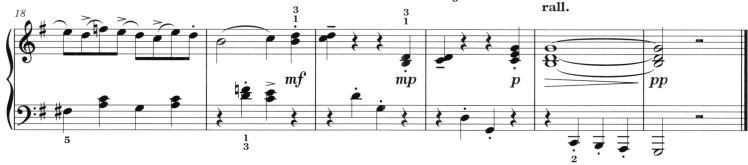

Peter and the Wolf (Петя и волк Petya i volk) is a folk tale for narrator and small orchestra, composed by Prokofiev (who also wrote the words) in 1936, the year in which he settled permanently in Moscow after many years abroad. It has become one of his most enduringly popular scores. Each character in the story is represented by a particular theme, played on a specific instrument: the Bird theme by flute, the Duck by oboe, Grandfather by bassoon, Peter by strings, the Wolf by horns, and the Cat (arranged here for piano) by clarinet. In this arrangement, the words of the story are included for interest – they should not be read aloud in the exam. You will have to listen to the rest of the piece to find out what happens next!

Gospel Flair

No. 43 from *Mini Jazz*, Vol. 1

C:3

Manfred Schmitz
(1939–2014)

Manfred Schmitz, composer of *Mini Jazz*, says: 'You'll have lots of fun "moving" into the exciting, wonderful world of jazz!' He adds: 'You can strike the accented notes a lot harder than you would in pieces by Bach or Mozart…your performance should reflect the fun you're having while playing!' In *Gospel Flair*, quavers should be straight, not swung. The fermata in b. 8 signifies the end, not prolongation (the chord is staccato!).

The German composer and pianist Manfred Schmitz studied at the Franz Liszt Academy of Music in Weimar, where he later taught (1968–84). After 1960, he often toured with his Manfred Schmitz Jazz Trio, and he also wrote a number of jazz-influenced pieces for children.